Under Water

The Northern Lakes

Photographs and notes by Douglas R. Stamm

THE UNIVERSITY OF WISCONSIN PRESS

Published 1977
The University of Wisconsin Press
P.O. Box 1379
Madison, Wisconsin 53701

The University of Wisconsin Press, Ltd.
70 Great Russell Street, London

First printing
Printed in the United States of America
The North Central Publishing Company
St. Paul, Minnesota

Designed by William Nicoll of Edit, Inc.

Library of Congress Cataloging in Publication Data

Stamm, Douglas R
Under water.

Includes bibliographical references and index.
1. Fresh-water fauna—Wisconsin—Pictorial works.
2. Fresh-water fauna—Michigan—Pictorial works.
3. Lake ecology—Wisconsin—Pictorial works.
4. Lake ecology—Michigan—Pictorial works. I. Title.
QL146.S75   574.92'9   76-53658
ISBN 0-299-07260-6
ISBN 0-299-07264-9 pbk.

To my grandfather, Chester Schumacher,
whose special wisdom and insight
have influenced those who know
and love him

Contents

Near-shore waters

Littoral zone

Open water

Pelagic zone

Camouflage
page 87

Night
page 95

Foreword

The freshwater lakes which are a familiar part of our northern landscape are generally thought of as places for recreation or as sources of income; and to most people the complex and varied life that flourishes in them is largely unknown. In this remarkable collection of photographs Doug Stamm opens up to us the hidden world that lies beneath the surface of these lakes, providing a graphic record of the aquatic organisms to be found there and giving us a look at their habitat and behavior. A musky lurking camouflaged in its cover or crayfish devouring a dead sucker by night are common occurrences in these lakes but they are sights not often seen by man. Precise observation of the individual creature, such as we have in these illustrations, is both the starting point for the appreciation and enjoyment of nature and the basis for the analysis of the intricate interactions in ecosystems now studied by ecologists and behaviorists. Much of what is shown here can be observed, by the naturalist or the summer vacationer who is seeking excitement and

knowledge in the lakes, without the use of expensive diving equipment — a face mask and snorkel will suffice for shallow water observations, which can yield a fascinating range of experience.

No two of these bodies of water are alike; there are thousands of lakes, with great diversity among them. In the softwater lakes aquatic communities are markedly different in number and species from those in the hardwater lakes, and often one need only drive a mile or two from one lake to another to see these contrasts. The curious and diligent observer can therefore constantly discover new associations of plants and animals, as well as different species. Moreover, he will learn, as he watches carefully, to detect the means by which animals communicate — by sight, sound, odor, or touch. The photograph in this book of the crayfish in its threatening posture, with pincers extended, shows us a striking example of visual communication.

The lakes in which these photographs were taken are relatively unspoiled, and can therefore serve as benchmarks against which adverse changes in the aquatic environment can be measured. Many of the lakes in our landscape have become so turbid from algae and sediment that underwater vision is impaired, and in some lakes native populations of plants and animals have suffered damage or destruction at the hands of man. Better understanding of lake ecology and greater knowledge of aquatic habitats on the part of concerned citizens as well as scientists and politicians is needed if the detrimental effects which civilization can have on our lakes are to be guarded against.

Many readers of this book will find that it has shown the way to new knowledge and perhaps new adventures. Some readers whose curiosity about these freshwater lakes has been aroused by this book may be stimulated to pursue a professional interest in hydrobiology. Others may be influenced to keep for their own enjoyment careful records of their observations, which can be valuable in assessing changes that occur in the environment. In this book Doug Stamm reveals the beauty and fascination of underwater habitats. Those who, as amateurs or professionals, follow him beneath the surface of the lakes will find reason to value these habitats more and to join in the efforts to preserve our aquatic resources.

Arthur D. Hasler
Director, Laboratory of Limnology
University of Wisconsin-Madison

Preface

The underwater photographs in this collection were taken over a three-year period in various northern lakes with different degrees of water clarity. This book does not attempt to portray a complete cross section of the life that inhabits these lakes, but rather to take a broad look through a camera's eye below their surface. It can only suggest the diversity, mystery, and beauty of this underwater world.

Not all the lakes contain everything presented here. Some of them do; many of them contain more. It was not possible to photograph all the various species of fish in these lakes: some live too deep, others are too shy, some are too scarce to be found. Many of the most common and most fascinating aspects of the underwater environment are pictured here, but there still remain many kinds of plants and animals, large and small, not included in this collection.

There are those of us who live near these lakes, fish in them, boat upon them, swim in them, or sit on their shores, and wonder what sort of place and what kind of life lie below their surface. It is for this reason the collection was made. I have attempted to expose for a moment their secret places and creatures.

These lakes are islands of water on the land, delicate and complex, a common sight, taken for granted, but still in many ways not very well known. I would like to think that as you page through this book you may perhaps come to a greater appreciation and better understanding of these lakes of the North and their inhabitants.

Doug Stamm
Madison, Wisconsin
July 1976

Note to divers and photographers

Photographing the more mobile subjects in this collection often proved to be a matter of patience, combined with the understanding that one does not sneak up on aquatic animals. As a diver enters the water he becomes an intruder, a large ungraceful creature spewing bubbles to the surface, no doubt quite inept in the eyes of the aquatic inhabitants. Almost every animal around you and far beyond the limits of your vision knows you are there. If you do get close enough for a good photograph it is only because the subject has allowed you to do so. More often than not, the best photographs are obtained when you move slowly, stopping often, allowing the subjects to find you. Many fish will approach a diver from the rear, curious to see what he is, but instinctively moving in from behind. This is especially true of the muskellunge. Next time you are below, go slowly and look behind you; you may see something quite amazing. And when you are there, leave underwater cover sites as you found them. You will conserve life and habitat.

I have included with each photograph in the collection photographic data for those who are interested or who wish to duplicate results. Unless otherwise specified, Kodachrome 64 film was used and shutter speeds were 1/60 second. The strobe used carries two light-output intensities rated in wattseconds (ws). The following equipment was used: Nikonos II camera with 35 mm lens; Subsea MK 100 strobe; Green Things Opal Eye wide-angle lens; S-2, S-3, S-4 closeup lenses; Aqua-Craft 1:1 and 1:3 extension tubes.

Acknowledgments

From the conception of this work through its evolution as a book there are many people who have assisted a great deal. From Dr. Warren Stuntz, Dr. William Schmitz, and Walter Haag of the University of Wisconsin Laboratory of Limnology and its Trout Lake Research Station, I have received encouragement, information, and support. To Tim Whitney, Mike Talbot, and Don Johnson for their critique of the material and to Nancy Schmaal, my eleventh-hour typist, I owe much thanks. And to Diane, who never doubted, I am truly grateful.

Introduction

In an age 50,000 years past a change descended upon the earth that would forever leave its mark on the North American continent. For unknown reasons the earth's climate began to cool. Winters gradually became colder and longer, and their snows reached farther south with each passing year. Coastal lands expanded as oceans began to shrink, their waters turned into polar snow which no longer melted. The earth's climate continued to cool, and plants and animals had to adapt, move farther and farther south, or die. As polar snows fell with increasing frequency, and the snowfields deepened, an ice layer formed beneath them and grew immense as centuries passed.

A new ice age had begun. Eventually a gigantic ice sheet expanded southward from the Arctic, moving only inches a year, pushed forward by the weight of the ice accumulating behind it. Ten thousand feet thick in places, it crept across Canada and into the northern United States as similar ice sheets extended over other areas of the world. Four times glaciers spread across North America from the Laurentian highlands of northern Canada, each time driven back by long intervals of mild climate, so that the whole of the glacial age extended over many thousands of years.

As the last glacier receded, it exposed the deep gouges it had made in the land and left mammoth ice blocks imbedded in the earth. Eventually these ice blocks melted, leaving more depressions in the land. The melting glacier to the north was the source of countless rivers that fed these depressions with water and with rock debris ranging from gravel and sand to the giant boulders which can still be seen today. Some of these depressions lost their water and are now valleys and lowlands. Others retained the water and became the "kettle" and "finger" lakes abundantly scattered through the northeastern part of the United States and eastern Canada.

These lakes today obtain their water from direct precipitation, springs, seepage through the ground, and, in some cases, from inflowing streams. Much of the earth material in which the lakes lie and through which the streams flow is either sterile bedrock or the rock debris originally brought south and left behind by the Laurentide glacier. That debris is granite and schist, hard and relatively insoluble. Thus the waters contain few dissolved minerals, and so are called "soft" water or "oligotrophic" lakes. In two dramatic ways, these lakes still show the influence of the glaciers that formed them long ago: in their clear water and in the kinds of life they contain.

The most basic forms of aquatic life, bacteria, plankton, and algae, require dissolved minerals in the lake water. Submergent vegetation requires many minerals for growth. With few minerals in these lakes such forms of life are not plentiful. The water is clear, vegetation scarce. With fewer of these basic forms there is less of what feeds on them — fewer microscopic animals of many kinds, fewer snails and clams that need minerals for their shells as well as bacteria and algae for their food. Larger animals that require these forms for food are also fewer — minnows, aquatic insects, tadpoles, and frogs. And at the top are the large predator fishes that depend upon the smaller creatures for their food. A chain of life exists here, one link depending on the next, and the last still depending on the first. There is still much life here, not so diverse in species and numerous as in the warm and turbid southern lakes, but no less important or intricate.

The lakes have countless links with the land. Many insects begin their life cycle in these lakes; loons and gulls use them; beaver and otter live with them; raccoon and mink feed on their shores; osprey and eagle feed from their surface. The chain of life extends beyond their surface, out onto the land, and back again. They are more than open spaces of water, and their dimensions extend far below their surface.

The lakes and their inhabitants have existed here for 10,000 years, gradually changing and adapting to nature's influence. That influence is slow and continuous and the changes are rarely visible to one generation of man. But the lakes are entering a new age, subjected to a new and accelerating influence; they are under the pressure now of man and his technology. Whether they will continue to co-exist with us depends upon how wisely and carefully we co-exist with them now.

Man has an instinctive attraction to water, and these northern lakes with their beauty and serenity bring millions of people to their shores. They are an important resource, for such waters are rare in the world.

Near-shore waters *Littoral zone*

Where land and water meet is a rich and vital
place in the lake environment. Here the
greatest abundance of visible life is found.
These waters are the shallowest and warmest in
the lake, encouraging the growth of vegetation,
and are often dense with submerged trees
felled by beaver, wind, and shore erosion.
These fallen trees, with their branches, logs,
and leaves, are essential to the existence of
many kinds of aquatic animals, providing them
with cover, shade, and food.

A leaning pine reaching into the water's edge illustrates the interface and merging of two environments. Shore erosion by waves has over many years washed away the soil supporting the pine and, with its lake-side roots no longer able to support it, it gradually dips deeper into the water. The tree thus slowly becomes part of the underwater environment and is converted into food and cover for the lake's inhabitants.

f8 at 10 ft (3 m), 1/30 second
Sparkling Lake, Wisconsin
September 1975

A young tree felled by beaver leans down the edge of a shoreline drop-off. Soon the beaver will strip it of its remaining branches; only the bare trunk will remain when they are through. The leaves and bark will either be eaten immediately or stored for winter, and the branches are destined to become part of a beaver lodge or dam. In areas of high beaver populations, near-shore waters are strewn with these remains.

f5.6 at 15 ft (4.6 m)
Unnamed lake,
Ottawa National Forest,
Michigan Upper Peninsula
August 1974

Suspended a few feet below the surface, a large pine log hangs motionless beneath a surface reflection of sky and trees. Only after many months or even years of gradually becoming water-logged will it settle to the bottom. Such giant logs, or ''dead heads,'' are common in lakes in regions once heavily logged, where they hang at various angles and levels, creating an eerie setting when seen from below.

f8 at 20 ft (6.1 m)
Clear Lake, Wisconsin
June 1975

A regular shoreline feature is the tangle of a wind-felled tree lying horizontal with the bottom and held there by its branches. It is in and around these "treefalls" (as the sunken trees are commonly called by divers and others who work and live with the lakes) that many forms of aquatic life will congregate. Submerged or partly submerged trees provide excellent cover for many fish species, furnish food for scores of aquatic insects, snails, and crayfish, and serve as a foundation for the growth of sponges and vegetation. And with the eventual complete decay of the tree, important nutrients are released into the water and taken up by aquatic plants and microscopic life.

f5.6 at 6 ft (1.8 m), wide-angle lens
Sparkling Lake, Wisconsin
July 1976

5

A view towards shore reveals the most prevalent type of near-shore terrain, which is in sharp contrast to the dense tangle of a treefall environment. The bottom here is strewn with rocks, boulders, and occasional logs, and vegetation is sparse. Lakes like this one, not lined by heavy forest, or having no inflowing streams, normally receive few nutrients from land. What few nutrients are available are first taken up and held by plants and plankton, and are not released again until the plant or animal dies. The waters of these lakes are clear but are unable to support much life.

f8 at 15 ft (4.6 m), wide-angle lens
Unnamed lake,
Sturgeon River State Forest,
Michigan Upper Peninsula
June 1976

6

The barren expanse of shoreline is broken here by the presence of a large submerged branch. Though providing little cover, it is all that is available to the small group of fish hovering nearby. Decreasing their vulnerability to predators is of prime importance to smaller fishes, which will use to the utmost any form of cover they can put between themselves and predators attacking them. In lakes which have little cover, the total number of fish and the number of species are both relatively small, but they are usually the maximum that the given cover will allow.

f5.6 at 20 ft (6.1 m)
Sparkling Lake, Wisconsin
June 1975

In 4 feet of water, a fallen tree attracts schooling perch and becomes a feeding area where they seek minnows and insects. A true schooling species, the yellow perch move in groups which are generally of the same size and age, with the older adults ranging further from shore. They continually roam during the day, moving inshore at morning and offshore at night, or swimming up and down in deeper waters. The young prefer shallower waters and will often school with near-shore minnows of similar size. Perch prefer clean, cool water with moderate vegetation, since their numbers within a lake tend to decrease as water turbidity increases or as vegetation decreases.

Adult perch can vary anywhere from 4 to 12 inches (10 to 30 cm) in length, depending on their abundance within a lake and the amount of available food, and under ideal conditions may reach ages of 9 or 10 years. The adults spawn in the spring as they school, the females depositing ribbon-like bands of eggs which are left to settle to the bottom. The hatching fry are preyed upon by all predator fishes and the adults are a favored food species of the northern pike and muskellunge.

The yellow perch occurs only in North America, primarily from the Hudson Bay south to the Great Lakes and from the northern Rocky Mountains east to the Atlantic. Through accidental and deliberate introduction, the perch is now present in many states south and west of its original range. In the Great Lakes the perch was one of the first freshwater species to be commercially fished, beginning in the 1850's, and it still sustains a large commercial fishery there and in the larger lakes of Canada.

Perca flavescens, Family Percidae
Common names: yellow perch, perch, lake perch, American perch, raccoon perch
French common name: perchaude

Angler record: 4 lbs, 3.5 oz (1.9 kg); New Jersey, 1865

f5.6 at 5 ft (1.5 m)
Sparkling Lake, Wisconsin
June 1975

Ambloplites rupestris,
Family Centrarchidae
Common names: rock bass,
northern rock bass, redeye,
redeye bass, goggle-eye
French common name:
crapet de roche

Angler record: 2 lbs, 2 oz (0.9 kg);
August 1971

f8 at 4 ft (1.2 m)
Clear Lake, Wisconsin
July 1975

Moving out from their beaver lodge cover, these rock bass curiously watch a diver in their midst. From a diver's perspective rock bass must be the most friendly of all freshwater fishes. They readily leave their cover to gather closely about a diver and can be fed by hand if the offering is made without quick movement.

As its name suggests, the rock bass prefers rocky, shallow water, where it uses vegetation, fallen trees, and beaver lodges and dams for cover. The adults tend to congregate and remain near a preferred beaver lodge or fallen tree, traveling as a school around their cover. The size of these schooling groups varies with the size of their particular cover. The larger their group, the bolder the bass become, but they still rarely venture far from their territory. They feed mainly on insects, crayfish, small minnows, and at times on their own young.

Spawning begins in late spring and early summer when the male digs a shallow nest near shore. He aggressively guards his nest from all intruders except the females of his species, which he attempts to attract and keep near the nest. The spawning completed, the female leaves the nest and the male remains to guard and fan the eggs. He stays with the hatched fry until they are able to leave the nest. As adults, the rock bass may range from 8 to 10 inches (20 to 25 cm) in length and reach ages of 10 to 12 years. Both adults and young are the prey of pike, muskellunge, and larger basses.

The native range of the rock bass was confined to east-central North America, but it has gradually been introduced into the western and southern United States as a game pan fish. It is still commercially fished in the Great Lakes, in the Mississippi River, and in Canada, where the province of Ontario is the major producer.

The favorite habitat of older and larger rock bass is beneath a log and in its shade. With age they leave the groups and, either alone or with a few others similar in age and size, they occupy quiet shaded places. These older bass are less curious than the young, and pay little attention to intruders.

f8 at 6 ft (1.8 m)
Sparkling Lake, Wisconsin
June 1975

Probably the most famous of treefall dwellers is the Great Lakes muskellunge. Once having selected a submerged tree for cover and shade, the muskellunge tends to claim it for his own and guards it from all intruders. Other habitats vary from beds of vegetation to the tangle of abandoned beaver lodges in shallow water. Very large individuals are occasionally found at depths to 50 feet. The older and larger muskellunge may lose their dark vertical markings, thus becoming "silver" muskellunge.

The muskellunge is habitually a solitary fish, living and hunting alone. It remains near its cover site, moving little except to search for food and even then rarely ranging far. When it sights prey it attacks quickly, taking almost any living animal its size will allow, including fish, crayfish, mice, shrews, muskrats, snakes, and waterfowl, both young and adult. Spawning begins in early spring and may last for several days. The females swim side by side with the males over heavily vegetated or flooded areas, depositing their eggs randomly as they spawn and then abandoning them.

"Muskellunge" is an American Indian word for a fish of great size and strength, a suitable name for one of the largest aquatic predators and game fish of North American freshwaters. The average muskellunge ranges from 30 to 46 inches (76 to 117 cm) in length, weighing 8 to 36 pounds (3.6 to 16.3 kg), and may live in excess of 30 years. A report dating from the early 1900's describes a muskellunge netted in Wisconsin weighing 102 pounds, but such a fish would be extremely rare.

The muskellunge is found in the cool, clear waters of three major watersheds in the United States and in Canada's southeastern lake basins and rivers. It is present in the Great Lakes watershed from Minnesota to the St. Lawrence River, in the Ohio River basin as far south as Kentucky, and in the Mississippi River between Wisconsin and Minnesota. Populations today are highest in the northern regions of Minnesota, Wisconsin, Michigan, and New York.

The muskellunge has not always been solely a sport fish. Its great size and its food quality made it a valuable commercial fish for over 60 years, but in order to keep its population high, legislation was passed allowing it to be taken only by hook and line.

Esox masquinongy,
Family Esocidae
Common names: muskellunge, maskinonge, Great Lakes, Ohio, Wisconsin muskellunge, musky, lunge, tiger muskellunge
French common name: maskinongé

Angler record: 69 lbs, 15 oz (31.8 kg), 64.5 in (163.8 cm); St. Lawrence River, September 1957

f5.6 at 8 ft (2.4 m)
Sparkling Lake, Wisconsin
June 1975

15

The northern pike, shown here moving out from vegetation, is another inhabitant of shallow and near-shore waters. Since they prefer vegetation to fallen trees for cover, pike are more abundant in heavily vegetated lakes and rivers. The pike waits well camouflaged in the vegetation for whatever prey passes by, and, like the muskellunge, the pike will take almost any living animal. A northern pike is capable of eating animals as much as one-third to one-half its own length, digesting the head of the prey while its tail still protrudes from the pike's mouth. Although a close relative of the muskellunge, the pike is less solitary in habit and has a greater cruising range.

When pike and muskellunge occur in the same lake, the pike are usually more numerous, since they are more successful competitors for food, space, and spawning sites. The pike spawns earlier in the spring in the same areas as the muskellunge, and the larger fry of the pike prey heavily on the muskellunge fry.

The northern pike is circumpolar in distribution in the northern hemisphere, reaching its greatest sizes in northern Europe and Britain. In North America the pike generally ranges from 18 to 30 inches (46 to 76 cm) in length. It may live as long as 26 years. European records claim weights up to 57.2 pounds (26 kg). There is a contested record of a Scandinavian pike weighing 74.8 pounds (34 kg).

Besides being a popular game fish, the northern pike supports an important fishing industry in Canada, which exports 80 percent of its catch to the United States. In Europe the pike is kept in enclosed areas in ponds and lakes and raised for food.

Esox lucius, Family Esocidae
Common names: northern pike, pike, great northern pike, jack, jackfish, pickerel, great northern pickerel, hammer handle
French common name: brochet, grand brochet

Angler record, North America:
46 lbs, 2 oz (21 kg),
52.5 in (133.4 cm);
Scanadaga Reservoir, New York,
September 1940

f4 at 6 ft (1.8 m)
Lake Salsich, Wisconsin
July 1975

Stizostedion vitreum vitreum,
Family Percidae
Common names: walleye,
yellow walleye, pickerel,
yellow pickerel, yellow pike,
pike-perch, yellow walleye pike
French common name: doré

Angler record: 25 lbs (11.4 kg),
41 in (104.1 cm);
Old Hickory Lake, Tennessee, 1960

f2.5 at 8 ft (2.4 m)
Clear Lake, Wisconsin
August 1975

In milky waters a school of large walleye travels among the branches of a daylight habitat. Since their eyes are relatively large and sensitive to light, they remain in the shade of sunken trees, vegetation, or deep water until nightfall. At dusk they move into sandy or rocky shallows and, with well-adapted night vision, they prey on whatever smaller fishes or insects they may find. The walleye is a schooling nomad, moving about a lake or river at night in a constant search for food. Each school may have its own spawning ground and summer territory. Individuals have been tracked roaming distances of up to 100 miles a month about their lakes.

In early spring, as lakes and rivers thaw, the walleyes begin their spawning runs by moving up tributary rivers or streams, many homing in on the same spawning ground year after year. In large lakes spawning takes place on coarse sand or boulder shoals. Far northern populations may not spawn at all in years when temperatures are too low. Males move into the spawning grounds first. When the females arrive, there is lively courtship behavior, including pursuit, pushing, and circular swimming. Suddenly the school rushes into shallow water, their eggs and milt broadcast over the bottom and abandoned. The spawning, involving one to three males per female, occurs at night and may be completed by morning. Adult walleyes generally weigh from 2 to 8 pounds (0.9 to 3.6 kg), but weights up to 15 pounds (6.8 kg) and ages up to 20 years are not uncommon towards the northern limits of their range.

The walleye is found along a line from northwestern Canada to the southeastern United States. It is today the most important commercially fished species and the most important sport fish of North American freshwaters. In the United States it is fished commercially in the Great Lakes and the Mississippi River.

The largemouth bass is another game fish that prefers the surroundings of near-shore shallows and sunken logs. This large largemouth, showing clearly why it is so named, rests in 3 feet of water. Largemouth often lurk alone like this in ambush for prey, or roam in groups through beds of vegetation, hunting smaller fishes, frogs, or perhaps a careless mouse found swimming at the surface.

Like the males of other members of its family, the male largemouth is the nest builder when spawning begins in late spring and early summer. In shallow water he uses his fins to fan a depression in the bottom 2 to 3 feet in diameter, carrying off in his mouth any small pebbles left in the nest. When a female is attracted and their spawning is completed, the male remains to defend the nest. Any approaching intruder within an area of 20 feet is quickly attacked and driven off. After the eggs hatch, the male guards the schooling fry until they disperse.

The adult largemouth bass averages from 2 to 6 pounds (0.9 to 2.7 kg), depending greatly upon its location in its range. In south-central to southeastern Canada, the northern limit of its distribution, it rarely exceeds 8 pounds (3.6 kg). The largest are found in Georgia and Florida. Because of its hardiness and desirability as a food and game fish, it has been introduced into almost all freshwaters of the United States, as well as into Europe, the Philippines, South America, Hong Kong, and South Africa.

In the United States and Canada the largemouth bass is a major game fish and was once an important commercial catch for both countries. In the United States it has long been a favorite for stocking farm ponds for food and sport, a practice now increasing in Canada.

Micropterus salmoides,
Family Centrarchidae
Common names: largemouth bass, northern largemouth bass, largemouth, black bass, largemouth black bass, green bass, bass, green trout
French common name: achigan à grande bouche

Angler record: 22 lbs, 4 oz (10.1 kg), 28.5 in (92.4 cm); Montgomery Lake, Georgia, 1932

f8 at 3 ft (0.9 m), strobe 50 ws
Prong Lake, Wisconsin
July 1975

This fingerling largemouth bass has ventured
from its shelter, an algae-laden sunken tree,
and stares intently at its reflection in the
camera lens. Only 3 inches long at this stage,
the fingerlings often group together in
vegetation or shoreline brush and fallen trees,
feeding on insects and smaller fishes. Their
curiosity about their own reflection and their
tendency to group together has given rise to
specially designed traps made of glass, which
are used by scientists in their studies of the
largemouth.

f11 at 12 in (30 cm),
S-4 closeup lens, strobe 50 ws
Prong Lake, Wisconsin
August 1975

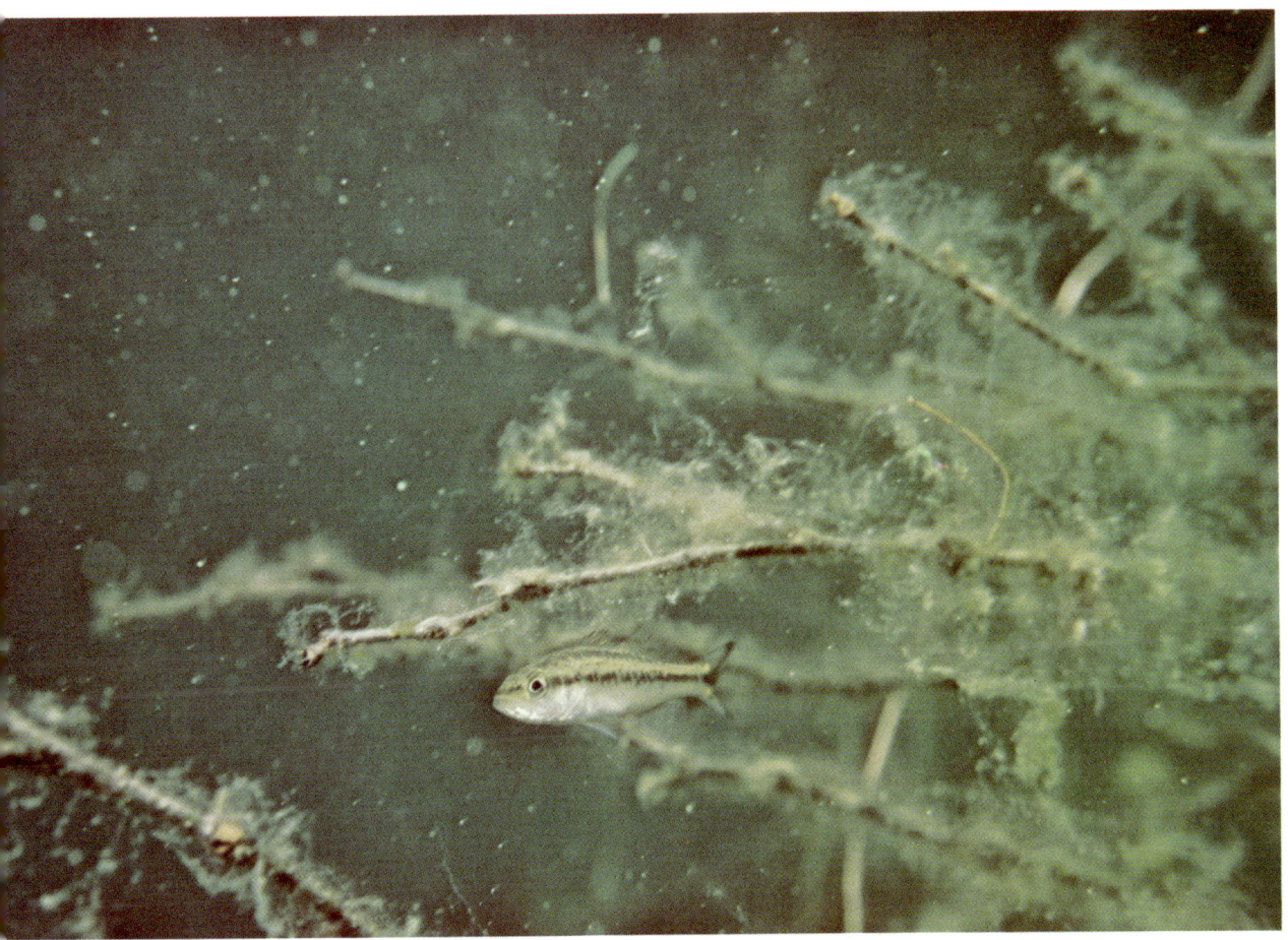

23

Lepomis macrochirus,
Family Centrarchidae
Common names: bluegill, sunfish,
bluegill sunfish,
northern bluegill sunfish,
blue sunfish, bream, blue bream,
roach
French common name:
crapet arlequin

Angler record: 4 lbs, 12 oz (2.2 kg),
15 in (38.1 cm);
Ketona Lake, Alabama, 1950

f8 at 3 ft (0.9 m)
Prong Lake, Wisconsin
June 1975

In the act of spawning, a pair of bluegills circle their nest in a bed of sand. In late spring and early summer the males gather near shore in nest-building colonies, fanning leaves and branches to create depressions down to sand and gravel. The males guard their nest, waiting for and attracting females, which gather at the edge of the colony when the nest building is completed. The female chooses her mate, swims over the nest, and the two bluegills circle, depositing eggs and milt into the depression. When spawning is completed the female is driven from the nest, and if she still holds eggs she will continue the ritual with another male. The males remain to guard the eggs and the hatching fry, which can number 225,000 in a single nest.

The bluegill prefers shallow, weedy, warm-water lakes, large and small, and is also found in rivers and large creeks if they are slow-moving and heavily vegetated. Bluegills feed mainly on insects, plant material, plankton, and smaller fishes, and are in turn fed upon by larger fishes. They grow to lengths rarely exceeding 12 inches (30 cm), but average much less in heavily populated lakes, where they become stunted. Maximum ages have been recorded at 8 to 10 years.

The bluegill is native to eastern and central North America, ranging as far north as the Great Lakes and south into Mexico. It has been introduced beyond its original range into most western states and also into Africa.

The bluegill serves as an important sporting pan fish in the United States and supports a Canadian fishing industry on the Great Lakes. It is commonly used as a forage fish, being stocked in ponds and lakes to support largemouth bass and northern pike.

A nest-guarding bluegill falls for an old trick as it chases the lead perch away from the nest. With the bluegill diverted, the trailing perch will dart through the nest, taking eggs and fry on each pass. Large schools of perch have been observed moving into bluegill nesting colonies, feeding heavily among the frantic and outnumbered nest-guarding males. Because of the abundance of eggs in each nest, such predation rarely prevents successful reproduction.

f5.6 at 5 ft (1.5 m)
Prong Lake, Wisconsin
June 1975

Lepomis gibbosus,
Family Centrarchidae
Common names: pumpkinseed,
pumpkinseed sunfish, yellow sunfish,
sunny, plunky, sun bass, pond perch
French common name: crapet-soleil

f8 at 3 ft (0.9 m), strobe 50 ws
Clear Lake, Wisconsin
June 1975

One of the more colorful of freshwater fishes is the pumpkinseed. This one is a 5-inch breeding male rising from its spawning nest in a darkly shaded cove. The pumpkinseed is similar in habits and feeding patterns to the bluegill and often the two species will interbreed, giving rise to fertile hybrids. Like the male bluegill, the male pumpkinseed creates and guards one nest in colonies with other males and will remain to protect the young, even carrying them in his mouth back to the nest if they stray. Under ideal conditions adults may reach lengths to 10 inches (25 cm) and ages to 10 years.

The pumpkinseed prefers clear, small lakes, ponds, or shallow bays in larger lakes that have brush and vegetation adequate for cover. It feeds primarily on insects, plankton, and smaller minnows and is itself preyed upon by larger predators. The pumpkinseed originally was found only in eastern North America in and around the Great Lakes, but it has been introduced into western areas of the continent and into Europe. In Canada the pumpkinseed is commercially fished both in large inland lakes and in the Great Lakes and is a favorite, easily caught sporting pan fish throughout its range.

A colorful 5-inch green sunfish peers from within a protective crevice among near-shore boulders, revealing the characteristic large mouth and emerald spots on the face. Rarely venturing far from such a habitat, sunfish are quick to dart into holes and spaces around boulders, sunken trees, and vegetation. They cautiously leave their cover in small groups in search of minnows and surface and aquatic insects, and when frightened often remain in groups, huddling tightly in the small cracks and spaces of their cover.

Green sunfish are associated with the shallows of rivers, ponds, and small lakes and have a propensity for overpopulating their body of water, resulting in stunted populations. Their lengths vary greatly, from as little as 3 inches (8 cm) in stunted individuals up to 12 inches (30 cm), and they may reach ages of 9 years. Rarely very large themselves, they fall prey to many larger fishes, primarily the basses.

In late spring and in some cases throughout the summer the green sunfish spawn among other pan fishes. Males guard a depression which they fan in the bottom and remain to protect the eggs and then to stay with the young for a short period. In Wisconsin, at least, the spawning green sunfish trigger spawning in a species of shiner, which are allowed to deposit their eggs among those of the sunfish.

The green sunfish ranges from South Dakota and Colorado eastward to New York and south to the Gulf of Mexico and into Mexico. The northern lakes are as far north as their distribution reaches and they are not commonly found there. In Canada they are present only in southern Ontario. Throughout its range the green sunfish is a sporting pan fish in waters where it grows to edible size.

Lepomis cyanellus,
Family Centrarchidae
Common names: green sunfish,
green perch
French common name: crapet vert

f5.6 at 8 in (20 cm),
S-2 closeup lens, strobe 100 ws
Devils Lake, Wisconsin
August 1976

In a latter stage of transition, a 6-inch green bullfrog tadpole rests in warm shallows near the shore. Almost ready to emerge from the lake, it now bobs occasionally to the surface for a quick gulp of air. As its lungs develop and its other frog features mature, it will take more air with each surface visit and gradually move closer to shore. It now grazes on algae and vegetation. Soon its tail will disappear and its hind legs will become stronger, allowing it to leave the water as a green bullfrog. As a fully grown adult frog, feeding on airborne insects, it may reach a length of 8 inches (20 cm).

The green bullfrog is native to the east-central half of the United States from southern Canada to Texas. It is present in almost all heavily vegetated lakes, ponds, and slow-moving rivers within this range. The northern lakes are the northern limits of its range and here, in the cooler water, it often must spend two years as a tadpole. In its southern range, along the Gulf of Mexico, the bullfrog is harvested and marketed for its large edible hind legs. Attempts to raise it commercially in the west and in Cuba, Taiwan, and Hawaii have so far proved unsuccessful, because of the time required for it to reach marketable size.

Rana catesbeiana, Family Ranidae
Green bullfrog

f11 at 14 in (36 cm),
S-2 closeup lens, strobe 50 ws
Sparkling Lake, Wisconsin
July 1975

A rarely obtained photo reveals a tadpole perching like a sparrow on a branch of a submerged tree. Not often is any large intruder allowed this close. When danger approaches, tadpoles usually swim quickly downward into the protective tangle of the tree.

Common visitors of submerged trees, they often rest in large numbers on underwater branches, looking very similar to a flock of birds. Tadpoles using these trees are usually those without developed hind legs and probably find resting on branches more comfortable than lying on the bottom. Moreover, since they appear as extensions of the branches, it is harder for predators to detect them.

f5.6 at 20 in (51 cm),
S-4 closeup lens, strobe 100 ws
Sparkling Lake, Wisconsin
July 1975

Floating through aquatic space, this 2-inch young painted turtle moves among dots of algae illuminated by sun and camera flash. By day the painted turtle basks lazily in the warm sun on logs or boulders, and usually only fright or hunger causes it to roam. It rarely travels far in its search for insects and vegetation, crawling slowly along on shallow bottoms and watching carefully for movement of prey. Ponds, quiet lakes, and slow rivers are the habitats of the painted turtle, and it is one of the more abundant turtles throughout its range.

In October and November the painted turtle goes into a form of hibernation, burying itself under water in mud or bottom debris, and remains there throughout the winter. In March the turtles begin to emerge from the bottom. Breeding begins immediately and may continue throughout the summer. Shortly after mating, the female seeks an open, relatively high location to bury her eggs, sometimes wandering several hundred yards from water. When she finds a suitable site, she digs a hole with her hind legs, deposits her eggs, then covers the hole with soil. Usually the eggs, unless disturbed by predators, will remain beneath ground until the following spring.

Once hatched from the eggs, the young turtles dig to the surface and instinctively crawl towards water.

Species of the painted turtle range as far north as southern Canada and across all of the northern half of the United States. In some areas the painted turtle is eaten by man, but its small size (12 inches, or 30 cm, at the maximum) discourages this form of predation.

Chrysemys picta, Family Testudinidae
Painted turtle

f16, 1:3 extension tube, strobe 100 ws
Trout Lake, Wisconsin
August 1975

One of the most interesting freshwater animals is the giant waterbug. For its size it is a remarkably voracious hunter. This 3-inch predator hides among floating vegetation, head down, tail just above the surface, waiting for its prey to pass by. At the proper moment it darts suddenly down, grasps its victim with its large raptorial front legs, pierces it with a sharp syringe-like mouth part, and injects a stunning venom. With its victim paralyzed, the giant waterbug sucks it empty of body fluids. It is capable of capturing fish several times its size, but it more commonly takes smaller fish, insects, crayfish, and tadpoles.

Well-adapted to its aquatic environment, the giant waterbug has flattened hind legs, making it a powerful, swift swimmer, and snorkel-like appendages at the tip of its abdomen for reaching above the surface to breathe air. Not content to be simply aquatic, it can leave the water and fly long distances. At night waterbugs are often seen flying around outdoor lights.

Members of the giant waterbug family are spread worldwide and live in almost all freshwater bodies. In Asia a species of the giant waterbug is boiled in salt water and eaten; it can be found for sale in San Francisco's Chinatown.

Genus *Lethocerus,*
Family Belostomatidae
Common names: giant waterbug,
fish killer, toe biter,
electric lightbug

f16, 1:3 extension tube, strobe 100 ws,
Kodachrome 25 film
Squash Lake, Wisconsin
July 1975

A large crayfish, claws down in curiosity and bluing with age, closely examines the camera with its antennae. Usually it is the old and large individuals that will calmly approach an intruder, since their size makes them relatively brave and free from predation.

The crayfish is mainly active at night, when it wanders about the bottom searching for food. With its antennae it feels vibrations and movement and in its clawed feet are organs for detecting food by taste. It has an efficient sense of smell and can sense and locate dead and dying animals. It will eat almost anything organic, from vegetation to its own species. Snails are a particularly desirable food for the crayfish, which devours them completely and thus obtains from the shells calcium necessary for its own exoskeleton.

In some areas the ranges of particular crayfish species are being artificially extended, possibly by fishermen using them for bait. When a species is introduced into a new area, its size or particular habits may allow it to become resistant to predation and so dominate and overrun the new habitat. Because of the crayfish's voracious appetite for vegetation and some fish eggs, overpopulations of introduced species are in places removing cover vegetation and possibly lowering the reproductive potential of some spawning fishes.

Almost all freshwaters of North America contain species of crayfish living beneath rocks, sunken logs, or in burrowed tunnels. In southern areas of the United States large crayfish are harvested and eaten for the lobster-like flesh in their tails and claws.

Genus *Orconectes*, Family Astacidae
Common names: crayfish, crawfish, crawdad, crab

f16, 1:3 extension tube, strobe 100 ws, Kodachrome 25 film
Sparkling Lake, Wisconsin
August 1975

Caught in the open during the day, this crayfish takes a defensive stance as the camera approaches. When attacked by a predator, the crayfish raises and opens its claws, or chelae, and waves them at the approaching fish, waiting for an opportunity to swim quickly backwards, propelled by its large flapping tail. Immediately upon touching bottom it resumes its defensive stance. This behavior is repeated until the predator leaves or the crayfish finds cover.

The crayfish is most susceptible to predation by fishes during the three days between the shedding of its old exoskeleton and the hardening of its new one. The newly molted crayfish is often lighter in color, very soft, and weak — characteristics recognized by predator fishes. The exoskeleton is replaced up to two or three times a year in younger, growing crayfish, and once a year or less frequently in older crayfish.

f11 at 7 in (18 cm),
S-2 closeup lens, strobe 100 ws
Trout Lake, Wisconsin
August 1975

43

A small clam has anchored itself in the sand, its syphon extended as it pulls water across its gills and food particles into its stomach. Members of this family of bivalve clams or mussels have no head, antennae, eyes, or jaws, and they move along the lake bottom by extending forward a foot-like muscle which slowly pulls the shell along. They are found in almost all freshwater lakes and rivers in North America, and in many places are harvested for their pearl-like shells.

Mussels reproduce during the summer in a manner that is unique among freshwater animals. The male sperm are drawn into the gills of the female through her syphon and fertilization and care of the developing clams take place there. Later in the summer these young clams, or glochidia, are discharged up into the water and fall to the bottom with their two shells spread wide open. Here they await the opportunity to clamp onto the fins, tail, or gills of a passing fish, for without contact with a fish, the glochidia would die. The skin or gills of the fish encyst around and entirely cover the still-developing mussel for a week to two months, depending on the species of clam. When its development is complete, the mussel breaks from the cyst, falls to the bottom, and begins its independent life.

The female of at least one mussel species is equipped with a peculiar flap-like device which is waved about as the parasitic glochidia are being released from her gills. As perch, basses, and other fishes nibble at this inviting flap, they are easily infested. Infestation rarely harms the host fishes, many of which are afterwards immune to it.

Family Unionidae
Common names: mussel, clam

f16, 1:3 extension tube, strobe 100 ws
Big Muskellunge Lake, Wisconsin
August 1976

Disturbed from its hiding place among sand and leaves, this odd creature swims near the bottom. This 1-inch naiad will have to go through 10 to 15 stages of development and spend from one to five years under water, depending on its species, before emerging from the water as an adult dragonfly. Equipped with a powerful, grasping mouthpart, the naiads either wait in ambush or stalk within striking distance of their prey, which includes insects and each other. They move rapidly with a jerking motion across the lake bottom by taking water into their internal gills and forcefully ejecting it behind. When ready to emerge as mature dragonflies, they crawl through the surface into the air on a plant or branch, and then break through their old shells. Once their wings unfold and dry, they are ready for flight as fully developed airborne dragonflies.

As naiads, dragonflies fall prey to fishes, birds, frogs, and to each other, but as terrestial adults they have few enemies.

Genus *Hagenius*, Family Gomphidae
Dragonfly naiad

f16, 1:3 extension tube, strobe 100 ws,
Kodachrome 25 film
Sparkling Lake, Wisconsin
August 1975

After landing on an emergent plant, this damselfly has walked down into the water to deposit her eggs almost 2 feet below the surface on the plant's stem. With her task completed, and if she is not eaten by one of any number of animals, she will climb back to the surface, dry her wings, and fly away.

In a cycle similar to that of the dragonfly, the eggs will hatch aquatic insects which will emerge later in the summer as airborne damselflies.

Order Odonata
Damselfly

f8 at 7 in (18 cm),
S-2 closeup lens, strobe 50 ws
Prong Lake, Wisconsin
June 1975

A bottom closeup reveals an elongated half-inch tube of sand concealing the developing larva of a caddisfly. Its "case" is made of sand or vegetation, depending on the species, and serves as armor against its predators. When undisturbed, the larva will extend its head and forelegs and crawl about the bottom, dragging its case behind. As summer progresses, the larva will emerge from the lake as an airborne insect. Found in lakes, rivers, and creeks, these insect larvae are an important food for many fishes, especially trout.

On the right, a snail shell lies on its side, concealing the snail, which remains withdrawn during the day.

Order Trichoptera
Caddisfly

f8 at 7 in (18 cm),
S-2 closeup lens, strobe 50 ws
Sparkling Lake, Wisconsin
July 1975

Covering the end of a submerged log is the most primitive of multicellular animals — the sponge. This is one of 30 species of freshwater sponges found in ponds, lakes, and streams in the United States and Canada. They form mat-like incrustations on rocks, logs, sticks, or leaves, and in some cases are lobed or branched. Species growing on the upper side of objects are green from symbiotic algae living in the outer cells of the sponge. Those sponges or areas of sponges not in direct sunlight will be tan, brown, or gray. Colonies of the freshwater sponge are usually small, thin patches covering a few square inches, but under ideal conditions they may cover many square yards. Sponges are most abundant in clear, quiet waters less than 6 feet in depth, but some species tolerate deep or fast-running water.

Internally, the sponge is a maze of interconnected spaces, channels, and chambers. Some of the chambers are lined with cells equipped with microscopic tails, or cilia, that whip back and forth, creating a constant current through the sponge. As water moves through, food particles are strained and digested. Supporting the delicate sponge is a skeleton composed of a great many needle-like spicules intertwined throughout the tissue.

Many insect larvae, mites, and snails can be found inside and outside the sponge, using it for cover and taking advantage of its current to catch their own food. Except for the larvae of one uncommon species of insect which suck the internal contents of the sponge, it has no natural enemies.

Family Spongillidae
Freshwater sponge

f8 at 14 in (36 cm),
S-3 closeup lens, strobe 50 ws
Little John Lake, Wisconsin
August 1975

As this small snail crawls over the edge of a submerged log, it carries with it a number of still smaller animals. A close look reveals the presence of green hydra which have attached themselves to the snail's shell. The hydra are similar in form and function to their saltwater relatives, the sea anemones, but are much smaller, being only 2 millimeters in height. Other freshwater species may reach heights to ½ inch (12 mm).

The hydra attach themselves to a surface and extend their tentacles containing stinging cells which can suddenly project filaments to ensnare or penetrate and poison their microscopic prey of zooplankton. The impaled prey are then digested in the tubular section of the hydra. Larger hydra may even capture and engulf larval fish much bulkier than themselves. In the first stage of digestion the fish appears to be covered by a thin film; the film is the hydra, its body stretched entirely around its prey. On the other hand, when endangered or irritated, the hydra can withdraw its tentacles and contract into a tiny ball.

The hydra are also capable of secreting gas bubbles that carry them to the surface. There they will hang upside down on the surface film, trailing their poisonous tentacles into the water below.

The hydra feed voraciously, grow rapidly, and reproduce by eggs or by sprouting buds that grow on their sides. The bud develops a mouth and tentacles and then separates from the parent.

Hydra may be gray, brown, or green, the green being due to algae living within the hydra. Hydra are present throughout the United States and Canada, living in ponds, rivers, lakes, and streams.

Chlorohydra viridissima,
Family Hydridae
Hydra

f16, 1:1 extension tube, strobe 100 ws,
Kodachrome 25 film
Big Muskellunge Lake, Wisconsin
August 1976

In these sunny, warm shallows, conditions have favored the growth of horsetails and water lilies around the remains of an old pier. This type of shoreline environment attracts many kinds of fishes, especially pan fishes and basses, and provides a habitat for countless smaller animals and insects.

Horsetail flourishes in the shallow areas of most northern lakes, where it can grow through the surface. It not only provides shelter for underwater life but also serves as food for waterfowl and moose, and in winter the top parts of the plant, protruding through the ice, are part of the diet of ruffed grouse.

Genus *Equisetem*, Family Equisetaceae
Common names: horsetail,
scouring rush

f11 at 15 ft (4.6 m)
Vandercook Lake, Wisconsin
June 1975

Genus *Nuphar*, Family Nymphaeaceae
Common names: yellow water lily,
spatterdock, cow lily

f5.6 at 6 ft (1.8 m)
Unnamed lake,
Michigan Upper Peninsula
May 1975

In early spring the yellow water lily sends its floating leaf to the surface and decorates an otherwise barren shallows. The lily is usually found in concentrations in shallow waters, sending tuberous roots beneath rock and sediments. From the roots grow new sprouts of the lily, forming large colonies along a shore. Each flower rises on its own stem, reaches above the surface, and fans out into the familiar form of the yellow water lily. The flower in turn becomes a fleshy fruit containing many seeds, which are spread by the waves and currents.

The yellow water lily benefits both aquatic and terrestial life. It serves as cover for frogs, basses, and fry fishes, and the undersides of the floating leaves provide shelter for insects and a foundation for the growth of algae. Its seeds nourish many bird species; stems, leaves, and flowers are fare for deer and porcupine; and its roots are dug and eaten by muskrat and beaver.

The yellow water lily is found in east-central North America from the Gulf of Mexico to northern Canada, and when it blooms it is one of the most attractive wild flowers of this region.

Later in summer as the lily's leaves float on the surface, the leaves at its base spread about the stalk and glow red in crystalline shallows. In a world of browns and greens, the leaves of the lily stand out as an especially beautiful part of the underwater environment.

f8 at 30 in (76 cm)
Unamed lake,
Michigan Upper Peninsula
June 1975

59

Extended from the main plant, this fleshy new stem and leaf of the water shield plant hangs loosely on a dying stalk. With wave action or collapse of the parent plant the new stem breaks off . . .

f16, 1:3 extension tube, strobe 100 ws,
Kodachrome 25 film
Prong Lake, Wisconsin
September 1975

. . . and drifts with currents and waves as it hangs in the water. Eventually it will settle to the bottom, and, if conditions are right, it will send its now-folded leaf to the surface and continue the cycle.

Smaller than its close relative the water lily, water shield is found in large colonies in shallow waters, often mixed with water lily. There it grows in dense beds, providing excellent cover for many fishes, especially the bluegill. As a common plant of northern lakes, it is a valuable source of food for waterfowl, moose, muskrat, and beaver.

Brasenia Schreberi,
Family Nymphaeaceae
Water shield

f16, 1:3 extension tube, strobe 100 ws,
Kodachrome 25 film
Prong Lake, Wisconsin
September 1975

The stems of water shield spiral to the surface, anchoring their floating leaves 10 feet above the bottom. As the water shield grows in such beds, the floating leaves provide necessary shade from the sun, which shines deep into the clear northern waters. For the many small fishes that inhabit the beds, the stems serve as defensive barriers against predators. A thin layer of protective film grows around the water shield and supports algae and aquatic insects. These in turn provide food for the fishes that live there. Lakes which have large beds of water shield around their perimeters and shoals are apt to contain large populations of pan fishes.

f22 at 8 ft (2.4 m)
Prong Lake, Wisconsin
July 1975

On the bottom, long abandoned and forgotten, lie the decaying remains of a rowboat. No longer of use to man, it is now a home for many aquatic animals. Countless crayfish seek refuge beneath its bottom; tadpoles often rest on its seats and gunwales; and snails cover its surface, grazing on algae.

f5.6 at 10 ft (3 m), wide-angle lens
Prong Lake, Wisconsin
July 1975

Open water *Pelagic zone*

Waters farther out from shore provide little
cover except for scattered beds of vegetation
and occasional sunken logs. At depths greater
than 20 feet even cover vegetation is absent
because little or no sunlight reaches those
depths and water pressures are too extreme for
large plant life. A small fish venturing into this
domain can be easy prey for the swift, cruising
muskellunge and pike. Yet smaller fishes and
other animals inhabit the vastness of open
water, each with unique adaptations of habitat
selection and behavior that allow them to
survive there.

Skimming the top of tall vegetation, these 4-inch golden shiners demonstrate a major form of adaptation for open-water survival — the adaptation of schooling. By remaining together and moving as one unit they offer no particular target to a predator and if attacked will dart at random in all directions and immediately regroup after each pass. Predators often make a pass at such schools, intently watching for behavior marking a sick or slower fish. Those members of a school which are relatively slow or which appear weak will normally be taken first. Predation on these fishes keeps the weak and the slow out of the breeding population and thus allows the stronger and better adapted to continue the species.

Golden shiners prefer clean, quiet waters, where they roam extensively, feeding in open water, primarily on plankton and surface insects. Their spawning occurs in spring, when they deposit and abandon their eggs over filamentous algae.

The range of the golden shiner is growing, and extends at present over all of the United States east of the Mississippi River, and in Canada in the southern waters of the central and eastern provinces. Its popularity as a bait fish for pike and muskellunge supports a large bait industry in these areas and has resulted in its accidental introduction into western regions of the continent.

Notemigonus crysoleucus,
Family Cyprinidae
Common names: golden shiner, roach, bream butterfish, eastern golden shiner, American roach, American bream, sunfish, dace, bitterhead, chub, gudgeon, young shad, windfish, goldfish
French common name: chatte de l'est

f8 at 10 ft (3 m)
Sparkling Lake, Wisconsin
August 1975

These minnows move quickly and school tightly, since their 2-inch length makes them easy prey for many larger fishes. The smaller the schooling species, the tighter and more organized their schooling must be.

It is not yet fully understood how the schools are led or how their direction is determined, but these minnows exhibit one characteristic which enables them to school as closely as they do. Running down each side is a dark line ending at the base of the tail. By always keeping the line of another schooling member in sight as a reference point and by relying on their sensitivity to movement vibrations, they can effectively move as one organism. Almost all schooling fishes have distinct bands, lines, or spots which they may use for this purpose.

Another survival mechanism employed by many schooling fishes is their reaction to an odor released by a killed or wounded member of their own species. The odor warns them of an attack on their species nearby, and the school will avoid that area until the odor has dissipated.

Minnows, unidentified,
Family Cyprinidae

f11 at 15 in (38 cm),
S-4 closeup lens, strobe 50 ws
Sparkling Lake, Wisconsin
July 1975

Silhouetted by the sky, this large gathering of bluegills illustrates grouping behavior in open water. Though not a true schooling species, they band together like this when they venture from protective vegetation in search of plankton. When approached by a large predator, the group crowds closer together, keeping a watchful eye on the whereabouts of the intruder, and moves towards cover or away from the predator's front. The motion of the bluegills is calm, precise, and free of abrupt movements which could invite an attack. Only with a sudden rush of the predator will the bluegills dart quickly. Large muskellunge have been observed moving slowly through such groups of bluegills, whose only reaction was to divide the group ahead of the muskellunge as it passed through and to merge again behind it.

f5.6 at 15 ft (4.6 m)
Devils Lake, Wisconsin
July 1974

Occasionally the grouping of different species will occur among smaller fishes; here minnows, bluegills, and small basses travel together outside vegetation. Later the basses, as adults, will prey on the minnows and bluegills, but for the moment they are equally vulnerable and move together, finding safety in numbers.

f5.6 at 5 ft (1.5 m), strobe 50 ws
Squash Lake, Wisconsin
July 1975

Secure in their man-made shelter, or crib, a large number of rock bass and young walleye congregate for the artificial but effective cover it provides in open water. In the winter these cribs are built on the ice at specific locations about a lake and, with the melting of the ice in spring, they sink and settle to the bottom. In lakes with little natural cover, construction of cribs has greatly increased populations of game fishes.

f8 at 4 ft (1.2 m), strobe 50 ws
Sparkling Lake, Wisconsin
July 1974

Cottus bairdi, Family Cottidae
Common names: mottled sculpin,
Miller's thumb, Columbia sculpin,
blob, gudgeon, freshwater sculpin
French common name: chabot tacheté

f8 at 12 in (30 cm),
S-4 closeup lens, strobe 100 ws
Trout Lake, Wisconsin
August 1975

When frightened in its open-water habitat, this 2-inch mottled sculpin displays an important behavioral adaptation. If it is pursued by an intruder and no cover is near, the sculpin dives into soft sediments, effectively creating its own cover — this one peers from beneath disturbed silt and a sunken stick. The sculpin is one of the few freshwater fishes to use this maneuver.

In cool depths of open water sculpin hide by day beneath rocks or logs and by night search for larval insects and bottom-dwelling organisms. They spawn in spring beneath their cover, the male becoming dark-headed as he courts the females. An attracted female will enter his nest beneath a rock and, while upside down on the ceiling of the nest, will deposit her adhesive eggs. She then leaves or is driven off. The male remains to guard the nest and either fans the eggs or positions the nest so that the natural current moves across them.

The mottled sculpin is common to cool or deep freshwaters, and ranges widely from the Great Lakes region south to Georgia, and in Canada from the east-central provinces to Labrador. Across its entire range the sculpin is a major source of food for trout.

75

This large bullfrog tadpole is an unusual sight in deep open water. Tadpoles are not long-distance swimmers, and their usual habitat is on the bottom in shallow near-shore waters. A very small percentage of tadpoles become adult frogs, since excursions such as this one outside their habitual domain may prove fatal if they are sighted by hungry predators. If he persisted in such ventures, the tadpole probably did not survive the summer.

f5.6 at 3 ft (0.9 m)
Sparkling Lake, Wisconsin
July 1975

The burbot, or freshwater cod, with its cod-like barbel on the underside of its chin, is rarely seen in spite of its abundance in these waters. It has been discovered here at dusk at the edge of a deep-water drop-off, moving into shallower water to feed.

Primarily a resident of deep cold lakes and northern rivers, the adult burbot hides under rocks and boulders during the day and roams at night to hunt. It is a voracious predator and gorges itself until its stomach grotesquely distends. In the Great Lakes, where it is found to depths of 700 feet, the burbot feeds heavily on the prey fishes of commercial and game species.

The burbot spawns in winter, usually near shore, in whirling masses of about 10 to 12 fish, the females carrying up to one million eggs. When spawning is completed, the eggs are abandoned. The abundance of eggs and hatching fry amount to a large food supply and are heavily preyed upon by many other fishes. The distribution of the burbot is circumpolar, extending across all of northern North America and Eurasia. North American burbot may reach 4 feet (1.2 m) in length and weights up to 19 pounds (8.6 kg), while Eurasian individuals reach much greater lengths and weights to 75 pounds (34 kg).

The appearance of the smooth-skinned, eel-like burbot, with its reptilian markings, combined with its reputation as a food competitor of game fishes, has unfortunately caused it to fall from favor as a food fish in North America. Like its cousin the saltwater cod, the burbot is a highly edible fish and is especially prized in Europe. Its liver, high in vitamins A and D, is in large demand when canned or smoked.

Lota lota, Family Gadidae
Common names: burbot,
American burbot, ling, eelpont,
maria, methy, lush,
lawyer, freshwater cod
French common name: lotte

f8 at 20 in (5.1 cm),
S-4 closeup lens, strobe 50 ws
Sparkling Lake, Wisconsin
June 1976

Micropterus dolomieui,
Family Centrarchidae
Common names: smallmouth bass,
northern smallmouth bass,
smallmouth black bass, black bass,
brown bass, green bass,
white or mountain trout
French common name:
achigan à petite bouche

Angler record: 11 lbs, 15 oz (5.4 kg),
27 in (68.6 cm);
Dale Hollow Lake, Kentucky, 1955

f8 at 20 ft (6.1 m)
Trout Lake, Wisconsin
July 1975

A large smallmouth bass, in its preferred surroundings, cruises over a sun-flecked plain in its continual search for food. Swift-flowing streams and clear, cool lakes with open shoals of clean sand, rock, and boulders are the areas associated with the smallmouth bass. Adults frequent rocky shallows in spring and later move to moderately deeper waters with cooler temperatures, feeding mainly on crayfish, minnows, and insects. The juveniles congregate in small groups in rocky shallows, commonly harassing crayfish many times their size. With winter the smallmouths move in groups to deeper water and remain there until spring, eating very little.

In late spring and early summer, the adult males move into sand, rock, or gravel areas near shore to fan nest depressions in the bottom. When the females arrive, there is lively courting behavior, including rubbing, nipping, and display. After spawning, the females depart, leaving the males to guard the eggs and young. The smallmouth male is one of the most aggressive nest defenders and attacks anything approaching his territory, whether it is a thrown stick or a larger fish.

The smallmouth varies from 8 to 15 inches (20 to 38 cm) in length and usually weighs up to 3 pounds (1.3 kg), though 5 to 7 pound (2.3 to 3.1 kg) individuals are not uncommon in the southern limits of its range. Large smallmouths up to 14 pounds (6.4 kg) and ages of 15 years have been netted by researchers.

Originally the distribution of the smallmouth bass was limited to the freshwaters of east-central North America, but because of its reputation as a game fish it has been introduced into lakes and streams throughout the United States, southern Canada, and in many places in Europe, Russia, and Africa.

Like many other game fishes of today, the smallmouth was once a commercial species taken by the ton with hook and line and by nets. Now it is strictly a sport fish, supporting a large sport fishing-tourist industry in the northern United States and southern Canada.

While hunting in open water at a depth of 25 feet, these two smallmouths bank away from an attack on a small crayfish, now safely hidden beneath a sunken log and a cloud of stirred sediment. This pair of smallmouth was sighted regularly over the length of a summer, always in the general vicinity of a group of sunken logs. In that area the logs were the only source of cover available to crayfish, and since crayfish constitute the major portion of the smallmouth diet, these two individuals had good reason to remain there.

Smallmouths have been observed traveling in pairs along opposite sides of a sunken log, flushing crayfish to each other. In areas frequented by divers, smallmouths have learned to follow them closely, watching for and taking an occasional crayfish that the divers flush into the open.

f5.6 at 5 ft (1.5 m), strobe 50 ws
Sparkling Lake, Wisconsin
August 1975

In the barren greenness of deep open water this large walleye, fins folded, rests among sand and boulders. The walleye waits in the solitude and shade provided by 40 feet of water for nightfall, when it will start hunting prey. As a walleye becomes older and larger, it on occasion will leave the younger schools and move into deeper water to rest alone on the bottom. The large size of older walleyes makes them virtually immune to all predation and the constant alertness which young walleyes share with other small fishes is not found in these older animals. Their habit of deep-water resting is especially prevalent in clearer, less vegetated lakes where shaded cover is less abundant. In this resting state a walleye can often be approached and touched, which apparently takes it by surprise, for it instantly bolts away and disappears.

f5.6 at 6 ft (1.8 m), strobe 50 ws
Clear Lake, Wisconsin
July 1975

A horizontal view in 12 feet of water reveals a layer of cloudy water below 4 feet of clearer surface water. The sharp line where the two layers meet marks the presence of the thermocline, or the boundary of cold and warm water. Above the thermocline the water is warmed by the sun and mixed by wind and waves. Below it the water is cold and still. The boundary is visible here because dust and debris sink through the warm water and float on or stay suspended in the denser, colder water. Also, many species of plankton seem to prefer colder temperatures, and will not rise into the warmer water above.

The thermocline is always present, though it is not always visible, in still, deep bodies of water, and gradually moves deeper as summer progresses. It often acts as an unseen barrier to many fish species, which will remain above or below it, depending on their temperature preference. The cooler weather of autumn causes the two layers to mix, and the thermocline disappears until the following spring.

f5.6, wide-angle lens
Clear Lake, Wisconsin
June 1975

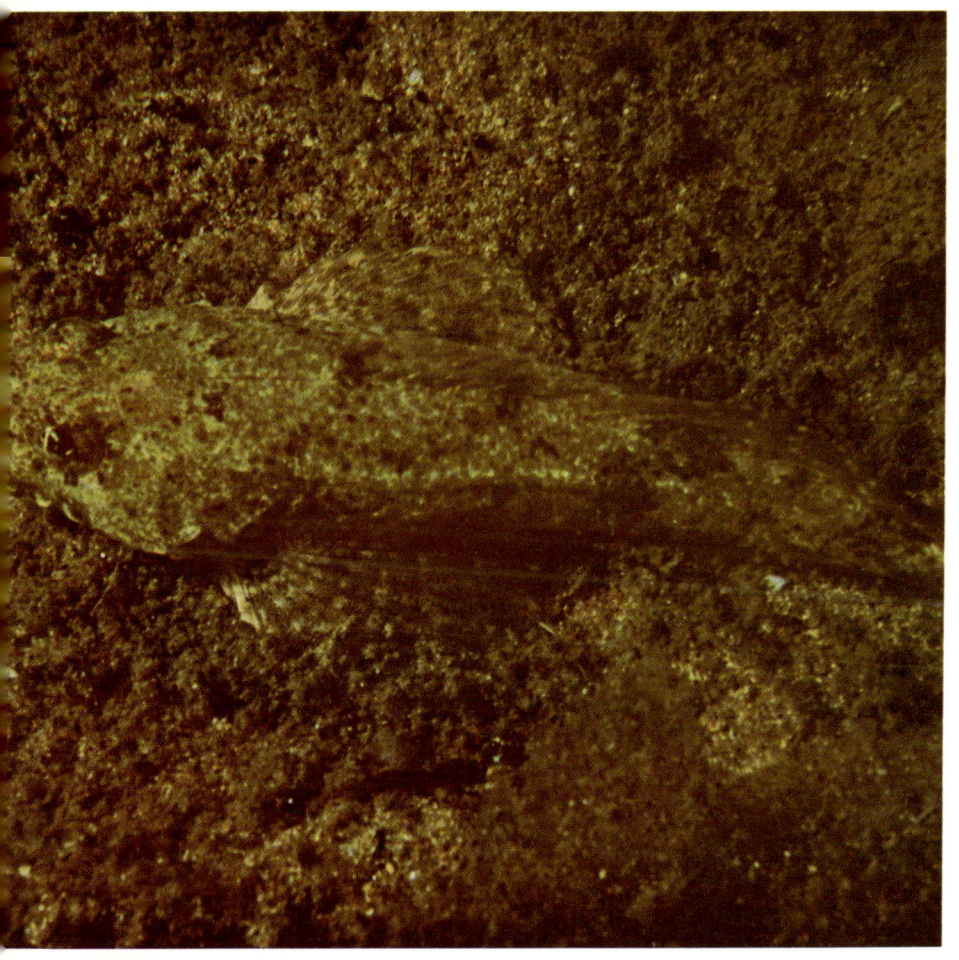

Camouflage

Nowhere is the use of camouflage better illustrated than in the northern lakes. With the supply of food limited and the numbers of animals which constitute the major proportion of that food relatively few, the survival of many animals depends greatly upon camouflage. Animals which make themselves conspicuous will not last long in the hungry world that is a lake. And camouflage is not limited only to the prey; the predator also must blend with its environment if it is to succeed in stalking or lurking in ambush for its prey. The coloration of freshwater animals is the result of the selection, over many thousands of generations, for the colors, shades, and patterns necessary for the survival of each species.

A large muskellunge hovers motionless, as if part of its cover, in the shade of a surrounding sunken tree. From such a place it may stalk slowly, moving only inches at a time, or bolt suddenly at passing prey. The muskellunge normally allows no other fish to share its cover, and all intruders are either eaten or driven out. If the muskellunge takes prey while away from its cover, it commonly returns with the prey impaled sideways on its large canines. Once back to its cover, the muskellunge will turn the prey in its mouth and swallow it head first. Because of the large amount of food each individual consumes and its solitary and territorial habits, there is not room for more than one muskellunge in any limited area or for many of them in any body of water.

The camouflage which this muskellunge, as a large predator, makes good use of now also served to protect it when it was a young fingerling and was potential prey even for its own species.

f4 at 7 ft (2.1 m)
Sparkling Lake, Wisconsin
June 1975

Doubled by its surface reflection, a small northern pike aligns itself with an overhanging branch, center. As it hovers without movement in flickering light and in the plane of the surrounding branches, a pike can easily escape detection by fishes swimming into the shelter of the sunken tree. This adaptation of camouflaged ambush is particularly characteristic of the Esocidae or pike fishes.

f8 at 15 ft (4.6 m), wide-angle lens
Unnamed lake,
Michigan Upper Peninsula
June 1975

A young rock bass displays the mottled markings that break up its profile and help conceal it as it hovers vertically near a stalk of vegetation. Juveniles will choose a particular piece of vegetation or small branch and move around it, through it, or up and down, and prodding or harassment rarely causes them to leave it. When danger approaches, the young rock bass moves into its small cover and remains still. When motionless inside the vegetation it is less recognizable as a fish and has a much better chance of escaping detection. As it reaches adult size it will lose these mottled markings, become more blandly colored, and move into the log-and-shade habitat of the adult.

f16, 1:3 extension tube, strobe 50 ws
Sparkling Lake, Wisconsin
August 1975

When this 2-inch mottled sculpin lies flattened against the bottom, in deep water, its outline is almost indistinguishable in the sand. The sculpin is a bottom-dwelling fish and a poor swimmer, moving occasionally in spurts or bolts across the bottom and never swimming up into the water. For it to catch enough insects, small minnows, and fry it must either flush them as it moves across the bottom or wait for them to move within its short striking distance. The coloration which allows it to blend with the bottom makes up for its inability to be a roving predator. More important, the sculpin's coloration helps conceal it from many other fishes that seek it as prey. Its swimming style is a peculiar one and it spends more time motionless than moving as it shifts under and around its rock-and-sand habitat. The odds that he will go unnoticed in the sand are in the sculpin's favor.

f16, 1:3 extension tube, strobe 100 ws
Trout Lake, Wisconsin
June 1975

A dragonfly naiad demonstrates its ability to blend with its surroundings as it rests on the bottom among sand and submerged leaves. The naiad is the prey of many aquatic animals, and hiding camouflaged amid and beneath bottom debris is its only defense. Its back is of a sandy, dusty complexion that exactly matches the color and texture of bottom sediments. The texture of its back also facilitates the growth of algae, further enhancing the naiad's ability to escape the notice of predators.

The tail of the naiad extends upper left; the head projects lower right.

f16, 1:3 extension tube, strobe 100 ws,
Kodachrome 25 film
Sparkling Lake, Wisconsin
August 1975

93

Night

The close of day does not bring an end to the activity within a lake. Instead it signals a changing of the animals that swim the water and roam the bottom. There are countless creatures that by day inhabit the sediments of lakes, hiding beneath rocks, logs, and leaves, and only with the fall of night stir and move out into the waters. Night brings out the scavengers to consume the dead and the dying and allows many creatures to seek their food, free from predators, most of which are inactive after dark. While night offers rest to many inhabitants of the lake, within the darkness the cycle of life continues.

A young walleye hunting minnows among shallow-water grasses at night makes a close pass across the camera's range. Their characteristic large and luminous eyes enable walleyes to locate and take their prey by the light of the stars and moon. As they roam through dark near-shore waters, they take advantage of resting and disoriented minnows and other smaller fishes.

f16, 1:3 extension tube, strobe 100 ws
Sparkling Lake, Wisconsin
June 1976

At night daylight predators like the muskellunge are dormant. Here a large muskellunge rests quietly, its only movement being the slow, stabilizing undulation of its lower fins. The muskellunge, like most other fishes, lacks eyelids, and so appears alert even while dormant.

Muskellunge tend to leave their daylight cover towards dusk and move into more open and unconfining areas to spend the night. In the darkness they often seem disoriented as they hover just off the bottom, tilting far to the left or right. They frequently bolt blindly and bump into vegetation or in some cases into the bottom when they brush against an unseen object or are touched by a diver's hand. Their instinctive fear of being touched or grasped is, perhaps, one explanation for their movement into open areas for the night.

f5.6 at 7 ft (2.1 m), strobe 100 ws
Sparkling Lake, Wisconsin
August 1976

At night the presence of snails becomes more evident as they come out of hiding and crawl along stems of vegetation to graze on algae. These quarter-inch snails are heavily preyed upon by many fishes, but after nightfall many of their enemies are inactive and the snails can move more safely about. Unlike clams, snails have eyes, antennae, and jaws for cutting food, and they are relatively mobile.

Shells of freshwater snails are primarily various shades of brown, and their thickness depends on the amount of calcium dissolved in surrounding water. These individuals, living in clear northern waters low in calcium, have thin transparent shells through which their bodies are visible. Snails of the two different families shown here carry both male and female reproductive organs and are capable of

Left side, Family Planorbidae
Right side, Family Physidae
Freshwater snail

f22, 1:1 extension tube, strobe 100 ws
Sparkling Lake, Wisconsin
July 1975

producing offspring alone. In most cases, however, mating occurs, each snail being both male and female to the other. After hatching from eggs laid in gelatinous masses, the tiny snails are immediately independent. Both families are common throughout North America.

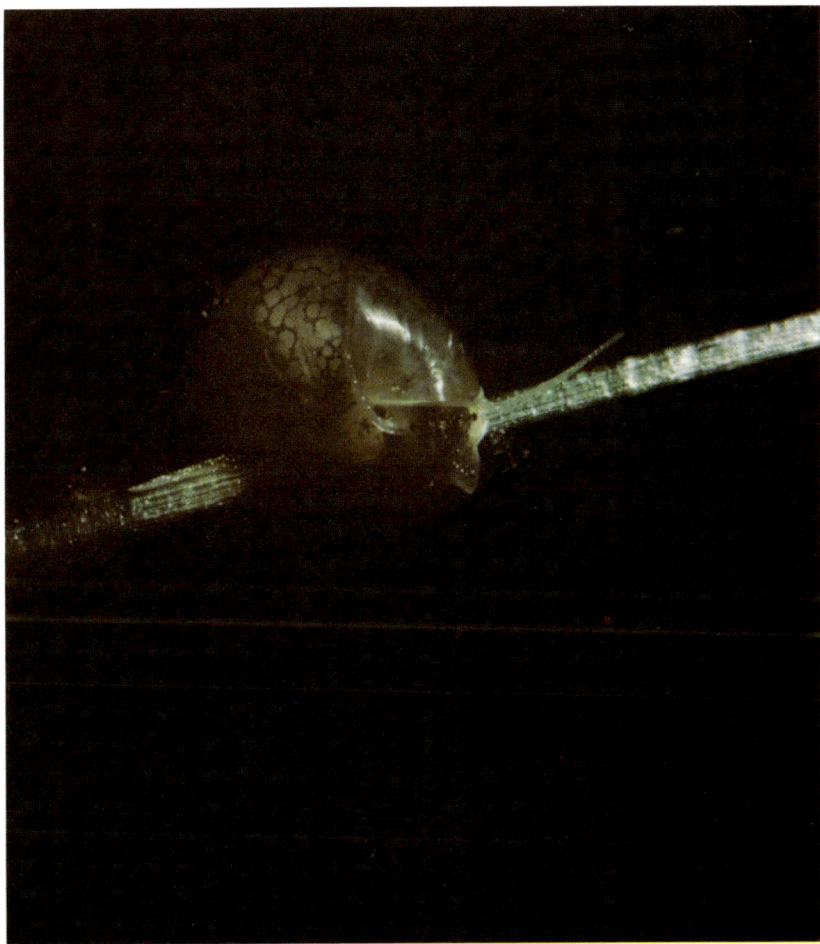

A 2-inch nymph of a mayfly, one of the most common of aquatic insect larvae, rises from beneath the sediments into dark water. Mayfly nymphs live on and below lake sediments, and, feeding in large numbers on plant debris, they literally change vegetative matter into animal matter. Fed upon by almost every aquatic predator, they are virtually defenseless but make up in numbers for their vulnerability.

The mayfly nymphs are aquatic for a few months to two years, depending on the species, and each species has its own time to emerge. When that time arrives, they rise from the sediments to the surface by the millions, break from their nymphal skin, and swarm as adult mayflies into the air.

The adult mayflies live for only a few hours or at most a few days, and their sole function is reproduction. After mating and depositing their eggs in the water, they die.

Order Ephemeroptera
Mayfly nymph

f16, 1:3 extension tube, strobe 100 ws,
Kodachrome 25 film
Trout Lake, Wisconsin
June 1975

In striking contrast with the blackness of night, a red watermite 4 millimeters long moves through the water, propelled by its rapidly flailing legs. Being relatively quite heavy, red watermites are well adapted for crawling on vegetation or the bottom and rarely resort to swimming; unless they swim vigorously or hold onto an object, they sink very quickly to the bottom. Shallow waters with rooted vegetation contain the greatest number of mites; although they do not feed on the vegetation, they seem to prefer it to the bottom.

Species of the red watermite are found worldwide, and nowhere are they heavily preyed upon by fishes. Their scarlet color seems to serve as a warning color, for some insect-eating fishes which have eaten one will thereafter avoid them, evidently reminded by the unusual color of an undesirable meal.

Genus *Limnochares*,
Family Limnocharidae
Red watermite

f16, 1:1 extension tube, strobe 100 ws,
Kodachrome 25 film
Sparkling Lake, Wisconsin
June 1975

Among all the underwater scavengers, the crayfish are surely masters. When night comes they leave their protective cover and wander in search of food. These crayfish have been guided by their acute sense of smell to a large dead sucker and are feeding everywhere on it. Some have already eaten the viscera, and the body cavity holds many crayfish eating towards the outside. Nearby, other crayfish are in a state of frenzy, crawling under and over each other, fighting, and attempting to eat everything and anything around them, including the camera and photographer. They are highly efficient scavengers, and with the coming of day only a skeleton remained of the sucker.

f8 at 20 in (51 cm),
S-4 closeup lens, strobe 100 ws
Trout Lake, Wisconsin
July 1975

Another scavenger by night is this species of leech, and here two leeches have wrapped around the body of a fungus-encrusted perch and feed on its flesh and fluids. During the day these leeches lie curled beneath logs and stones, and at night they stretch to their full lengths, up to 18 inches (46 cm), and swim in a graceful, undulating manner as they seek out their food. These *Haemopis* leeches feed primarily on small invertebrates and carrion, but occasionally attach themselves to frogs, fishes, and even to man, especially at skin abrasions or cuts. Some members of this genus of leeches will leave the water and crawl a quarter of a mile on moist ground, feeding on invertebrates, earthworms, and carrion.

Leeches, like snails, have both male and female sex organs, but must mate to reproduce. In early spring after a good meal copulation begins, and cocoons of eggs are laid throughout the summer. After a variable period of growth the young leeches emerge from the cocoons and become independent.

These leeches, only one of almost 50 species in northern North America, abound in warm, protected shallows where plants, stones, and debris provide concealment. The genus to which they belong is widely distributed and common throughout the northern United States and Canada.

Genus *Haemopis*, Family Hirudidae
Common names: leech, bloodsucker, horse leech

f22, 1:3 extension tube, strobe 100 ws
Sparkling Lake, Wisconsin
June 1975

Among the scavengers there is competition for the limited number of dead and dying animals, and a one-sided battle ensues here for food. While crayfish feed ravenously on the dead sucker, a leech swims towards the fish in an attempt to attach itself and feed. Each time the leech approached the sucker, however, the frenzied crayfish seized it and tried to devour it as well. No match for the powerful claws of the crayfish, the leech eventually retreated and swam away to search for more accessible food.

f8 at 20 in (51 cm),
S-4 closeup lens, strobe 100 ws
Trout Lake, Wisconsin
July 1975

Illustrating one of the most curious phenomena of fish behavior, these perch rest at night in the crotches of sunken tree branches (left) and, if small enough, will back into the end of submerged pine boughs (right), secure for the night. Large schools of perch have been observed swimming into sunken trees at dusk, occupying virtually every available nook and cranny. They more commonly spend the night scattered about the bottom on sand and debris, but they seem to prefer a hard substrate when it is available. In one instance a large number of perch were discovered resting from bow to stern on the gunwales and seats of a sunken rowboat. In areas with high populations of night-marauding crayfish and leeches, this behavior may protect the perch from their forays.

f22, 1:3 extension tube, strobe 100 ws
Sparkling Lake, Wisconsin
July 1975

A brilliantly colored painted turtle is rudely awakened by the intruding camera from his night's rest in a submerged tree 2 feet below the surface. In a state of rest it may spend the entire night below water, rarely if ever needing to surface for air. During the cool nights of northern summers, shallow waters are often warmer than the air and at dusk the turtle moves to the bottom or into sunken trees. When it finds a suitable site it tucks in its feet and head and sleeps until dawn.

f16, 1:3 extension tube, strobe 100 ws,
Kodachrome 25 film
Unnamed lake,
Michigan Upper Peninsula
June 1976

And finally, by the light of day, a fisherman sits at the edge of his boat and peers into the water. What he sees is as out of perspective as he appears from below. Beneath him exists a silent and elusive world of intricate life and beauty, only a small part of which has been photographed and described here.

f16 at 6 ft (1.8 m)
Clear Lake, Wisconsin
June 1975

113

Selected references

In writing the notes which accompany the photographs in this volume I have drawn upon both personal experience and information from many published sources. For the reader who is interested in knowing more about the lakes and their inhabitants, the following books are particularly recommended:

Lakes and fishes

Coker, R. E. *Streams, Lakes, Ponds*. Chapel Hill: The University of North Carolina Press, 1954.

Hubbs, Carl L., and Karl F. Lagler. *Fishes of the Great Lakes Region*. Ann Arbor: The University of Michigan Press, 1958.

Scott, W. B., and E. J. Crossman. *Freshwater Fishes of Canada*. Bulletin 184. Ottawa: Fisheries Research Board of Canada, 1973.

Invertebrates

Pennak, Robert W. *Fresh-Water Invertebrates of the United States*. New York: The Ronald Press Company, 1953.

Ward, Henry Baldwin, and George Chandler Whipple. *Freshwater Biology*. 2d ed. New York: John Wiley and Sons, 1965.

Vegetation

Fassett, Norman C. *A Manual of Aquatic Plants*. Madison: The University of Wisconsin Press, 1957.

Other books that I found helpful include:

Carr, Archie. *Handbook of Turtles*. Ithaca: Comstock Publishing Associates, 1952.

Cochran, Doris M., and Coleman J. Goin. *The New Field Book of Reptiles and Amphibians*. New York: G. P. Putnam and Sons, 1970.

Eddy, Samuel, and James C. Underhill. *Northern Fishes*. Minneapolis: The University of Minnesota Press, 1974.

Leviton, Alan E. *Reptiles and Amphibians of North America*. New York: Doubleday and Company, 1971.

Marshall, N. B. *The Life of Fishes*. Cleveland and New York: The World Publishing Company, 1966.

Needham, James G., and J. T. Lloyd. *Life of Inland Waters*. Ithaca: Comstock Publishing Company, 1916.

Needham, James G., and Minter J. Westfall, Jr. *Dragonflies of North America (Anisoptera)*. Berkeley and Los Angeles: University of California Press, 1954.

Nikolsky, G. V. *The Ecology of Fishes*. London and New York: Academic Press, 1963.

Schechter, Victor. *Invertebrate Zoology*. Englewood Cliffs, N.J.: Prentice-Hall, 1959.

Usinger, Robert L., ed. *Aquatic Insects of California*. Berkeley and Los Angeles: University of California Press, 1956.

Vesey-Fitzgerald, Brian, and Francesca Lamonte. *Game Fish of the World*. New York: Harper and Brothers, 1949.

Whiteley, Derek, David Nichols, and John A. L. Cooke. *The Oxford Book of Invertebrates*. London: Oxford University Press, 1971.

Index to illustrations